ISBN 0 85079 125 1

AN EXPRESS BOOKS PUBLICATION

£1

Printed by Eyre & Spottiswoode, Cosham, Hants. & co-ordinated by Roeder Print Services Ltd.

Ladies and gentlemen, on my right (Beau Peep speaking), I give you the fortunate duo to whom has fallen the unparalleled privilege of recording my astounding adventures in the Foreign Legion. If the lads have a fault (and they do) it's their irreverent tendency to dwell on the farce which is inescapable with characters like Egon, the world's worst cook, Sergeant Bidet, Sopwith the Camel, Mad Pierre, and, or course, that shining specimen of the slobotariat – mon camarade, Dennis!

Roger Kettle (writer) and Andrew Christine (artist)

MY BANISHMENT IS OVER. I HAVE BROUGHT YOU THE HEAD OF AN ENEMY WARRIOR!
500

LET US SEE IT.
YOU DOUBT MY WORD?!

THERE IT IS! WON IN MORTAL COMBAT!
FLIP!

ALL RIGHT, IT'S A PINEAPPLE, BUT THERE'S NO NEED TO BE RUDE.

HAIL! THE FIERY GOD RISES IN THE HEAVENS...
501

...BRINGING ANOTHER DAY OF WARMTH AND HOPE!

I WILL SING TO HIM THE ANCIENT SONG OF WELCOME!

OH, THE SUN HAS GOT HIS HAT ON

LONG AND FAR HAVE I WANDERED IN MY SEARCH FOR TRUTH.

AND WHAT HAVE I GAINED ? NOTHING !
502

THOUGH, I MUST ADMIT, I'VE GOT QUITE A NATTY SUNTAN.

OH, NO! BAD FORTUNE!

WHEN THE HAWK SOARS IN THE NORTH, YOU WILL LOSE A PRIZED POSSESSION!

503

THANK GOODNESS! I THOUGHT I'D LOST MY SWEETIES!

IN MY TRAVELS I HAVE LEARNED MANY THINGS.

LIKE, THERE'S NOTHING TO TOUCH A GOOD DRINK WHEN YOU'RE THIRSTY.
504

NOT OVERLY SPECTACULAR, I ADMIT, BUT THERE YOU HAVE IT.

AH! THE STARS AT NIGHT!

SO BIG SO BRIGHT.

DUM-DUM-DUM-DUM.

DEEP IN THE HEART OF TEXAS
CLICK!

COME AND PLAY DOMINOES.

ER... NO, THANKS, PIERRE. I'M READING.

DO YOU THINK YOU'LL BE ABLE TO READ WITH A BOX OF DOMINOES UP YOUR NOSE ?

DOUBLE SIX TO START, EH ?

YOU MADE A MISTAKE THERE, PIERRE. YOU PUT A FIVE AGAINST A TWO. YOU CAN'T DO THAT.

CAN'T DO WHAT ?

NOT UNLESS YOU REALLY WANT TO.

508
HAH! DOUBLE FOUR! MY GAME IF I'M NOT MISTAKEN!

CRUNCH!

I'M MISTAKEN.

YOU'VE PLAYED A DOUBLE THREE.

THERE WE ARE. A THREE-SIX I'M OUT!

SMACK!
509

SILLY ME! IT'S A TWO-SIX! THE OTHER SPOT WAS BLOOD.

AHA!

UNLUCKY DOMINO THAT.
WHY?

PEOPLE WHO PLAY IT END UP TOOTHLESS.

THANKS FOR THE GAME OF DOMINOES, PIERRE. YOU WON FAIR AND SQUARE.

YOU MUST TEACH ME THAT STRATEGY YOU USED IN THE FIFTH GAME.

YOU KNOW— THE STEP-OVER LEG-LOCK.

LET'S HAVE A QUIZ GAME TO PASS THE TIME.
RIGHT!
5/2

OKAY, WHAT'S THE CAPITAL OF JAPAN ?
THE NILE!

YOU'RE UNBELIEVABLE.

HA-HAH! YOU DIDN'T THINK I KNEW IT, DID YOU!

THIS IS GOOD FUN HAVING A QUIZ. I'LL ASK YOU A QUESTION NOW.
5/3

WHAT TIME IS IT ?

IF WE'RE GOING TO HAVE A QUIZ, I'D BETTER BE QUESTION-MASTER. DO YOU AGREE?

I SHOULD KNOW THAT ONE.

RIGHT, I'LL ASK YOU TEN GENERAL KNOWLEDGE QUESTIONS AND YOU GET ONE POINT FOR EVERY CORRECT ANSWER.
RIGHT!

WHO WROTE "A TALE OF TWO CITIES?"
OH... UM...ER... CHARLES...

YES! GO ON!
OH! WHAT'S HIS NAME? CHARLES... CHARLES...

...HAGGERTY! CHARLES HAGGERTY WANTS TO SEE YOU ABOUT ORGANIZING THE RAFFLE!

HERE'S YOUR LAST QUESTION, DENNIS — I'LL MAKE IT EASY.
5/6

WHICH ANIMAL DO WE GET BACON FROM?

I'LL GIVE YOU A CLUE — IT'S NOT THE SAME ONE WE GET EGGS FROM.

DRAT. I WAS GOING TO SAY HORSES, TOO.

SO MUCH FOR QUIZ GAMES. YOU GOT ALL TEN QUESTIONS WRONG.

I DID NOT! YOU ONLY MADE UP THE ANSWERS!
5/7

I STILL SAY I WAS RIGHT ABOUT THE PENGUINS!

IN FACT, I'LL PROVE IT! THERE'S SOME CIRCLING OVERHEAD NOW!

YOU'RE NOT MAKING WINE AGAIN, ARE YOU ?
YUP.

I WON'T MAKE THE SAME MISTAKE THIS TIME, THOUGH.

THE LAST VINTAGE, ALTHOUGH FULL-BODIED WAS A TRIFLE DRY FOR MOST PALATES.
518.

SO I'VE HARDLY PUT **ANY** CLEANING FLUID IN.

THERE ARE MANY SECRETS IN WINE-MAKING, DENNIS.

LIKE, FOR EXAMPLE, THE LENGTH OF TIME BETWEEN BOTTLING A WINE AND DRINKING IT.
519

THAT SHOULD DO IT !

THIS WINE-MAKING LARK IS ALL TRIAL AND ERROR, DENNIS.
520

YOU'LL HAVE NOTICED THAT I ERADICATED THE PROBLEM OF DRYNESS BY ADDING A CERTAIN FRUITY QUALITY.

THOUGH I FEEL THE COLOURING COULD BE LIGHTENED JUST A SOUPCON.

DAMN BOOTPOLISH STAINS EVERYTHING.

WHAT'S ALL IN THIS STUFF, BEAU?
DENNIS, DENNIS!

NEVER ASK A GENIUS HOW HE CREATED HIS MASTERPIECE!
521

YOU'RE ABSOLUTELY RIGHT, BEAU!

I MEAN, WE WOULDN'T ASK BEETHOVEN HOW HE PAINTED THE 'MONA LISA'.

THAT'S IT!
522

I'VE BEEN TRYING TO THINK WHAT I DID WRONG WITH THE WINE — IT'S THE GRAPES!

I SHOULD HAVE PUT SOME IN.

HERE IT IS!
GOOD!

523
IT WAS IN MY POCKET ALL THE TIME.

BIT WORRYING WHEN YOU CAN'T FIND YOUR HAND.

EGON, IS THIS FISH?
524

GLOOP

FUMBLE

NAH, THAT'S STEW. THE FISH HAS BONES IN IT.

EGON!

IT IS NOT MY INTENTION TO CAST EVEN THE TINIEST OF DOUBTS ON THE QUALITY OF THE FEAST BEFORE ME...
525

BUT I THINK THE MILK'S ON THE TURN.

EGON, THIS SOUP IS TEPID.

SCOOP!

SLURP!

NO IT'S NOT – IT'S OXTAIL. IT'S A BIT COLD THOUGH.
526

I'VE...ER... BOUGHT YOU A PRESENT, EGON – IT'S A COOK BOOK.
GOOD COOK
527
HERE, SOME OF THESE RECIPES ARE A BIT FANCY.
GOOD COOK
I CAN'T DO FANCY DISHES, I MEAN, WHAT ARE THOSE THINGS THERE?
GOOD COOK
THOSE ARE FRIED EGGS, EGON.
GOOD COOK

THAT COOK BOOK YOU GAVE ME IS TERRIFIC — I'VE MADE COQ AU VIN.

COQ AU VIN! TERRIFIC! I LOVE CHICKEN!
528

WELL, I THOUGHT I'D TRY TO PLEASE Y—

CHICKEN?

THAT NEW COOK BOOK HAS CHANGED MY LIFE.
529

I THOUGHT I'D TRY SCAMPI FLAMBÉ IN CREAM SAUCE.

THEN I THOUGHT, WHY BOTHER?
GLOOP!

DOWN, SOPWITH, DOWN! DOWN! DOWN!

KLUNK!
530

UP, SOPWITH, UP! UP, BOY, UP!

OKAY, SOPWITH LET'S GO!

HEY-HUP! HAH! LET'S HAVE A BURN-UP!
531

YEEE-HAH! ATTABOY, SOPWITH!

FIRST, PUT YOUR LEFT LEG FORWARD ABOUT A FOOT...

HEY-UP! HUPPITY-HUP! YEE-HAH!

WHOA! EASY, BOY, EASY!

WE SEEM TO BE SUFFERING FROM A LACK OF COMMUNICATION.

I'VE TAKEN ALL I'M GOING TO FROM YOU!

DENNIS! COME HERE!

DO YOU KNOW WHAT ANIMAL PSYCHOLOGY IS?
NO.

WELL, NEVER MIND. JUST HOLD MY JACKET WHILE I PUNCH THIS CAMEL.

I'LL TEACH YOU TO DO WHAT I SAY! PUT THEM UP!
BEAU! WAIT A MINUTE.

YOU CAN'T GO AROUND FIGHTING CAMELS. LET ME TRY TO TALK TO HIM.

HELLO, THERE! I WAS —
PTOO!

DIVERT HIS ATTENTION WHILE I PUNCH HIM!
JAB!
JAB!

I DON'T THINK WE SHOULD TELL ANYONE ABOUT THIS, DENNIS.
I AGREE.

I MEAN, IT DOESN'T SOUND TOO GOOD — "TWO LEGIONNAIRES BEATEN UP BY A DROMEDARY."

I DON'T KNOW ANYTHING ABOUT THAT— I WAS TOO BUSY FIGHTING OFF THAT DAMN CAMEL.

I'M SENDING YOU TWO OUT ON DESERT PATROL.
US?

IT'S ALWAYS US! ALL THAT BLAZING SUN AND BURNING SAND! WELL, WE'RE NOT GOING!

ALL RIGHT. I'LL HAVE YOU SHOT FOR DISOBEYING AN ORDER.

LET'S SEE - WE'LL NEED A TENT, KIT-BAGS, PLENTY OF WATER, OF COURSE...

ARE YOU SURE YOU REMEMBERED EVERYTHING?
OF COURSE!

THE MAPS? THE COMPASS?
YES! YES!

YOU DIDN'T FORGET THE COOKING STUFF?
NO, I DIDN'T!

I SOMETIMES THINK YOU THINK I'M STUPID!

I FEEL REALLY WIDE AWAKE, BEAU.
538

I'M NOT THE LEAST BIT SLEEPY.

EVEN AFTER ALL THAT WALKING, I'M NOT THE LEAST BIT TIRE—
ALL RIGHT, DENNIS!

"AND WHO'S BEEN EATING *MY* PORRIDGE" SAID DADDY BEAR....

IT'S A FUNNY THING, BEAU, BUT I WAS—
DENNIS! SHUTUP!
539

I CAN'T SLEEP.
COUNT SHEEP OR SOMETHING!

...HALLO! THERE'S ANOTHER ONE! WAIT A MINUTE IT'S A COLLIE DOG! MUST BE THE SHEPHERD'S, THERE'S ONE THOUGH! HE'S A BIG CHAP....

Z

BEAU!
EH? WHAT D'YOU WAKE ME UP FOR?

WHAT HAPPENS IF YOU'RE COUNTING SHEEP AND YOU ACCIDENTALLY COUNT THE SAME ONE TWICE?
DO YOU SEE THIS RIFLE, DENNIS?

ONLY JUST— MY EYES ARE BEGINNING TO CLOSE.

HOW WAS THE PATROL?
OK.

ANYTHING ODD OR UNUSUAL TO REPORT?

YES, THERE WAS— ABOUT FOUR O'CLOCK THIS MORNING.

I GOT THIS FUNNY SENSATION IN MY ELBOW, PROBABLY NOTHING, OF COURSE, BUT....

DOESN'T THE SIGHT OF THIS SET THE HEART SOARING, DENNIS?

SUNDAY AFTERNOONS AT HOME... THE SOUND OF WILLOW AGAINST LEATHER!

I ONCE MADE A CENTURY BEFORE TEA!
PROD

I ONCE MADE A TOY FORT BEFORE BREAKFAST!

BOWL ME A COUPLE AND WE'LL SEE HOW GOOD YOU ARE.
RIGHT.

WATCH OUT! ER... WHY NOT! ER... SO WHAT!

I BELIEVE YOU'RE TRYING TO SAY 'HOWZAT.'
CLICK!

YOU BOWL AN OVER AT ME. THAT'S SIX BALLS.

SINCE WE'VE NO FIELDERS, I'LL CONCENTRATE ON IMPROVING MY DEFENSIVE TECHNIQUE.

BEFORE WE START, HAVE YOU ANY QUESTIONS?

YES, WHY AREN'T WE IN THE PUB?

I KNOW YOU'RE NOT VERY SURE OF THE RULES, DENNIS, BUT JUST GIVE IT A TRY.

CLUNK!
SWISH!

WELL DONE, DENNIS! GOOD BOWLING!

NOW NORMALLY I WOULD HAVE BEEN OUT BUT FOR SOMETHING CALLED THE 'NO-BALL' RULE.

ARE YOU SURE YOU WANT TO BAT?
YUP.

WELL, I MUST WARN YOU I'M A BIT OF A DEMON BOWLER SO WATCH YOUR OFF-STUMP!

THAT'S A POINT. SHOUDN'T I BE WEARING SOMETHING?

WHAT'S THIS YOU'RE PLAYING?
IT'S...ER...CRICKET, PIERRE.

IT'S A GENTLEMAN'S GAME. I DON'T THINK THEY PLAY IT IN YOUR NECK OF THE WOODS.

IT'S SO SIMPLE EVEN YOU'D UNDERSTAND IT! YOU START BY...

SMACK!

...CLUBBING A BIG MOUTH TO THE GROUND USING A WILLOW BAT.

DENNIS!
HECTOR!

BEAU! COME AND MEET MY BROTHER, HECTOR!

GOOD HEAVENS, THERE'S SURELY NOT ANOTHER ONE LIKE DENNIS!

HALLO, BEAU! IT'S A PILGRIMAGE TO MEET YOU!
THERE IS.

MY BROTHER, HECTOR, IS STAYING HERE FOR A FEW DAYS BEFORE BEING TRANSFERRED

YES, I DECIDED TO JOIN UP WHEN I HEARD HOW WELL OUR DENNIS WAS DOING.

MUM WAS SO PROUD WHEN YOU TOLD US YOU'D MADE COLONEL.

TELL ME, BEAU—
WHILE HE'S AWAY—
HAS OUR DENNIS
BEEN BEHAVING
HIMSELF?

550
WELL, YOU KNOW,
HECTOR—THE
OCCASIONAL
FAUX PAS.

AND WHAT OF IT, EH?
I LIKE THE ODD GLASS
OF WINE MYSELF!

HAVE YOU GOT THOSE
THINGS I ASKED YOU
TO BRING FROM
HOME?
YES.

THERE
YOU ARE!
TEDDY!
551

THOUGHT I'D BRUSH UP
THE OL' BAYONET
PRACTICE.

SO THERE'S ACTUALLY THREE OF YOU? YOU'RE TRIPLETS?
YEP!

552
MUM STILL CAN'T TELL US APART.

IT'S SILLY BECAUSE, FOR A START, MAVIS IS TALLER THAN US.

CHEERIO, HECTOR! ALL THE BEST!

YOUR BROTHER WILL MAKE A FINE LEGIONNAIRE, DENNIS. A MAN TO BE PROUD OF.
553

JUST LOOK AT THAT! HE'S HARDLY CRYING AT ALL NOW!

DEAR ME, DENNIS—THOSE FEET OF YOURS ARE A BIT OFF!

MY FEET DON'T SMELL! IT'S HIM ROUND THERE!

HOI, YOU! ABOUT THOSE FEET OF YOURS...

WE WERE JUST SAYING HOW BEAUTIFULLY SHAPED THEY WERE.

IT'S IMPOSSIBLE SHARING THIS PLACE WITH MAD PIERRE— HE SMELLS LIKE A WARTHOG!

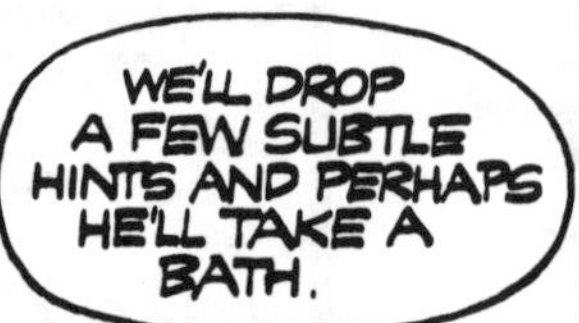
WE'LL DROP A FEW SUBTLE HINTS AND PERHAPS HE'LL TAKE A BATH.

HELLO, SMELLY.

I'D LIKE TO THINK, PIERRE, THAT AS FRIENDS WE COULD SPEAK FRANKLY TO EACH OTHER.

SO I'M SURE YOU WON'T MIND IF I MAKE A TINY COMMENT ON YOUR PERSONAL HYGIENE.

IT'S JUST THAT...
SMACK!
556

LET'S HAVE ANOTHER OF THESE FRANK TALKS REAL SOON, PIERRE!

Y'KNOW, IN ALL THE TIME WE'VE BEEN HERE I DON'T THINK I'VE SEEN MAD PIERRE TAKE ONE BATH

557
NEITHER HAVE I.

AT LEAST HE WASN'T THERE THE DAY I HAD MINE.

WE'VE GOT TO DO SOMETHING ABOUT PIERRE. THIS PLACE SMELLS LIKE A CAMELS' CONVENTION.

I KNOW! I'LL TELL HIM IF HE DOESN'T TAKE A BATH I'LL PUNCH HIS EAR!
558

A GOOD IDEA, DENNIS, BUT FOR ONE THING...

...I DON'T HAVE A PLUNGER TO GET YOU BACK OUT OF THE PLUG-HOLE.

ER... HELLO, PIERRE. DENNIS AND I HAVE BEEN HAVING A LITTLE CHAT.

WE FEEL THAT, LIVING AS CLOSELY AS WE DO, YOU TEND TO SMELL...ER YOUR HYGIENE...ER...

...WELL, DENNIS IS BETTER WITH WORDS THAN I AM...

PLEASE TELL ME YOU DIDN'T REALLY SAY "EVER HEARD OF SOAP AND WATER, STINKY?"
559

PEOPLE WILL MARVEL AT THE WISDOM I HAVE GATHERED ON MY TRAVELS.

"THERE HE GOES" THEY WILL CRY. "THE WISEST MAN IN THE WHOLE WORLD!"
560

I WILL NEED A NEW NAME SO THAT SEEKERS OF WISDOM CAN COME TO ME.

BOBBY BRAINS THE DESERT WHIZZ KID!
CLICK!

PEOPLE WILL COME FROM STRANGE LANDS TO HEAR ME SPEAK MY WORDS OF WISDOM.

THEY WILL ASK ME THE SECRET OF LIFE AND I WILL TELL THEM.
561

THEN MAYBE I'LL FINISH OFF WITH A SONG.

GREAT CROWDS WILL GATHER TO HEAR MY WISDOM AND I WILL SAY...
562

"... I WOULD HAVE BROUGHT YOU FIGS BUT I GOT MY DATES MIXED UP!"

GOOD IDEA TO HIT THEM WITH A FEW GAGS EARLY ON.

AHA! A SEEKER OF WISDOM!
563

GREETINGS! YOU WISH TO KNOW THE SECRETS OF LIFE? FEAR NOT! ASK ANYTHING OF ME AND YOU SHALL LEARN!

DID YOU DROP THIS HANKY?

LET ME TELL YOU SOMETHING.

YOU CAN TAKE A CAMEL TO WATER BUT DON'T COUNT YOUR BRIDGES.

DON'T YOU GO AROUND CLAIMING THAT AS YOUR OWN!

BEFORE YOU STANDS THE WISEST MAN IN THE WORLD.

ALL RIGHT, WALKING IN A STRAIGHT LINE, HOW LONG WOULD IT TAKE TO GO ROUND THE WORLD?

HA! HAH! IMBECILE! YOU THINK YOU CAN FOOL ME WITH TRICK QUESTIONS!

TEN MILES DOWN THE ROAD AND YOU'D FALL OFF THE EDGE!

BON JOUR, MINE HOST! A BOTTLE OF BEST VINO FOR MY LITTLE FRIEND AND I!

THIS SOUNDS PROMISING— "FROM ONE OF THE WORLD'S GREATEST WINE MAKING REGIONS..."
566

"... CLEETHORPES."

IT WAS DEFINITELY A GOOD YEAR, THAT.

567
YOU SURPRISE ME, DENNIS. BECAUSE OF THE BOUQUET ? THE TEXTURE ? THE FULLNESS OF FLAVOUR ?

NO—THAT WAS THE YEAR I MET MAVIS SMITH BEHIND THE BIKE SHED.

LET'S HAVE A LOOK AT YOUR HANDS, DENNIS.

568
TSK! THAT'S A BIT WORRYING!

WORRYING! WHY?

THEY NEVER GO INTO YOUR WALLET.

I CAN'T SEEM TO CATCH THE BARMAN'S ATTENTION.
569

CHOP, CHOP BIG EARS! LET'S HAVE SOME SERVICE BEFORE I GIVE YOU A BLACK EYE!

BAR
HE'S VERY NIMBLE ON HIS FEET FOR A BIG LAD.
CLACK! CLACK! CLACK!

IT WAS YOU WHO GOT US THROWN OUT SO YOU GO IN AND APOLOGISE.
BAR
510

SORRY ABOUT THAT BIG-EARS. NOW, LESS OF YOUR LIP AND BUY US A DRINK.

THAT'S THE LAST TIME I HUMBLE MYSELF FOR ANYONE.
BAR
CLACK! CLACK! CLACK!

I'D LIKE TO APOLOGISE FOR MY FRIEND HERE.

WHAT HE SAID WAS MEANT IN JEST AND WE'D LIKE YOU TO JOIN US FOR A DRINK.

HE'S LET US OFF, SO FOR GOODNESS' SAKE, DON'T SAY ANOTHER WORD.

BAR
WELL, HIS WINE DOES TASTE LIKE BOILED UP SOCKS.
CLACK! CLACK! CLACK!
511

KEEP A SPECIAL LOOKOUT FOR SABOTEURS TONIGHT.
BOATERS?

NOT "BOATERS," YOU IDIOT! SABOTEURS! PEOPLE WHO INFILTRATE OUR DEFENCES AND SABOTAGE THINGS!

WHAT, IN BOATS?

REMEMBER TO KEEP AN EYE OUT FOR THE SABOTEURS.
WHAT DO THEY LOOK LIKE?

GENERALLY THEY WEAR BOWLER HATS AND CARRY SIGNS WHICH SAY, "I'M A SABOTEUR."

WHAT ELSE?

WHAT DO THESE SABOTEURS DO, BEAU?
574

WELL, THEY GET BEHIND OUR LINES AND TRY TO DESTROY EQUIPMENT AND SUPPLIES.
LIKE FOOD?

THEY TEND NOT TO BOTHER TOO MUCH ABOUT SANDWICHES, DENNIS.

DENNIS, WHAT ARE YOU DOING?
WATCHING FOR SABOTEURS.
575

AREN'T YOU BECOMING A LITTLE OBSESSED ABOUT THIS? I MEAN, THEY'RE HARDLY LIKELY TO STROLL THROUGH THE FRONT GATE.

I'M NOT OBSESSED! IT'S JUS...
CLIP!

I GET IT! PRETEND TO CUT YOUR NAILS THEN — BINGO! — THE TELEPHONE WIRES ARE DOWN!

IT'LL TAKE A SMART SABOTEUR TO GET PAST ME!

YESSIR! ONE STEP AHEAD – THAT'S ME! HE'D HAVE TO BE UP EARLY TO SLITHER PAST ME! YESSIR!

I'D LIKE TO SEE ONE TRY TO GET PAST OL' HAWKEYE!

BEAU, D'YOU KNOW ANYTHING ABOUT THIS ROPE?

WELL DONE!

WHILE YOU TWO WERE ON DUTY, SABOTEURS SET FIRE TO THE SUPPLY ROOM!
OH, NO!

WHISPER

ER...BEHIND THE POTATOES, THERE WERE SOME... ER... MAGAZINES. DO YOU KNOW IF THE... ER... FIRE... ER...

YOU TWO WILL LEARN DISCIPLINE IF IT'S THE LAST THING I DO!

JUST A MINUTE THERE, SERGEANT!
578

YES?

COULD YOU SCRATCH MY NOSE, PLEASE?

I SPY WITH MY LITTLE EYE SOMETHING BEGINNING WITH 'S'
579

DENNIS, WE'VE BEEN THROUGH THIS BEFORE! IT'S EITHER SAND OR SKY!

NOT THIS TIME IT ISN'T.

SHOO! SHOO! GO AND SEE BEAU!

580
BLOW ON IT! BLOW IT AWAY!

PHOO!

I HOPE, FOR YOUR SAKE, YOU HAVEN'T UPSET IT.

THE MAIN THING, DENNIS, IS NOT TO PANIC.

WHAT IF IT BITES ME?

DON'T BE STUPID! SCORPIONS DON'T BITE—THEY STING!
581

GUESS WHAT THE NEXT QUESTION IS...

THE ONLY WAY TO GET IT OFF IS TO JERK YOUR HEAD QUICKLY.
SHH!

READY? 1-2-
582

-3!

IT WORKED BEAU! YOU'RE A GENIUS!

HERE COMES THE SERGEANT, BEAU!
583

DON'T MOVE, PEEP. I'LL SHOOT IT OFF WITH MY RIFLE.

WHAT?

WORKS EVERY TIME.

THE LOCAL SCOUTS REFUSE TO GO ON.

THEY CLAIM TO HAVE SEEN A LARGE APE-LIKE CREATURE SCUTTLING ABOUT THE DESERT.

THEY SAID IT WAS CALLING YOUR NAME.

HE KEEPS MUTTERING THE WORD 'DORIS.'

YOU MEAN THIS DORIS OF YOURS IS SOMEWHERE OUT HERE LOOKING FOR YOU?
YES.

MY GOD! ANYTHING COULD HAPPEN TO HER IN THIS HELL-HOLE!

D'YOU REALLY THINK SO?

THESE FOOTPRINTS WERE MADE BY MY DORIS. I FEEL SICK.

DON'T BE RIDICULOUS! HOW CAN YOU POSSIBLY TELL THAT THESE ARE HER FOOTPRINTS?

THE SCRAPE MARKS LEFT BY HER KNUCKLES.

THERE SHE IS— MY DORIS. SHE CERTAINLY DOESN'T GET ANY PRETTIER.

FOR GOODNESS SAKE, PEEP, SHE'S COME THOUSANDS OF MILES TO SEE YOU! YOU MUST AT LEAST SPEAK TO HER!

HELLO, DORIS.

MY DORIS IS TAKING HER CLOTHES OFF TO BATHE IN THE OASIS. YEUK!

MAYBE I COULD SHOOT HER WHILE SHE'S WALLOWING IN THE MUD.
PEEP!

THROUGH SHEER LOVE AND COURAGE THAT WOMAN HAS COME THOUSANDS OF MILES TO BE WITHIN A HUNDRED YARDS OF YOU!
588

YOU DO IT! I'LL NEVER HIT HER FROM THAT RANGE!

YOU MUST ADMIT ABOUT MY DORIS— HER UGLINESS TAKES THE BREATH AWAY.

GREETINGS! IT IS I! I THE UBIQUITOUS TRAVELLER! I, THE WISE MAN WHO SPEAKS OF THE SUN, THE MOON AND THE STARS!

STONE ME! WHO'S THE CRUMPET?
589.

SUCH BEAUTY! SUCH FULLNESS OF FIGURE! I WOULD GIVE MUCH MONEY FOR SUCH A WOMAN!
NOW JUST A MINUTE.

THAT'S MY DORIS DOWN THERE! A BRITISH WOMAN! AND WE DON'T HAPPEN TO SELL OUR WOMEN LIKE CATTLE!
5.90

A POUND?
SOLD.

OH, BE STILL, FOOLISH HEART!
LOOK AT HER! THE-ONE-THEY-CALL-DORIS SO GRACEFUL AS SHE WASHES IN THE OASIS.
5.91

WATER NYMPH! COME JOIN ME IN YONDER TENT!

THAT'S MY DRESS YOU'RE TALKING ABOUT, SQUIRT!

THE-ONE-THEY-CALL-DORIS IS THE MOST BEAUTIFUL WOMAN I'VE EVER SEEN!

THE ELEGANCE OF HER NECK! THE SUPPLENESS OF HER CHINS!

LISTEN YOU LITTLE CREEP, I'M GETTING OUT OF THIS WATER SO TURN YOUR BACK OR YOU'LL BE EATING KNUCKLES!

AND MODEST WITH IT!

ARE YOU TELLING ME YOU SOLD YOUR DORIS TO THAT NOMAD FOR A POUND?
YES.

THAT'S THE MOST OBSCENE THING I'VE EVER HEARD!
OH, ALL RIGHT! I'LL GIVE HIM SOME CHANGE!

THE ANGEL THAT YOU SOLD ME — THE-ONE-YOU-CALL-DORIS HAS GONE. SNIFF!
REALLY?

SHE HAS EYES ONLY FOR YOU AND SAYS SHE COULD NEVER LOVE ME. MY HEART IS HEAVY SOB!
594

ER... LOOK, I'M REALLY SORRY. IS THERE ANYTHING I CAN DO?

GIVE ME MY QUID BACK.

SO MY DORIS HAS REALLY GONE?
ALAS, YES.
595

SHE HAS GONE TO LOOK FOR WORK ON THE COAST SO SHE CAN FINANCE A PROPER SEARCH FOR YOU.

SNIFF! THAT SUCH DELICATE HANDS SHOULD BE PUT TO WORK!

DON'T WORRY. BULLDOZER DRIVERS WEAR GLOVES THESE DAYS.

A BOTTLE OF WINE, SQUIRE!

HERE, WHAT'S THIS ? DON'T TELL ME YOU'VE UPPED THE PRICES AGAIN !

AND DON'T TELL ME THE INGREDIENTS ARE MORE EXPENSIVE 'COS THEY AREN'T!

WELL, I SUPPOSE THE PRICE OF PARAFFIN HAS GONE UP A BIT.

IT'S QUIET IN HERE TODAY.

ONE MISSES THE OCCASIONAL DEBATE ON LIFE'S INTRICACIES.

X☆◎! HE'S PUT HIS ☆◎✳◎◎☆!! PRICES UP!

SCARF!
NO.

GIRAFFE! THAT'S IT! GIRAFFE!
NO.

598

ALLOW ME, DENNIS.

ANOTHER CARAFE, PLEASE.
CLICK!

ANY MINUTE NOW—"HERE, IS THAT THE TIME?"

HERE, IS THAT THE TIME?
"I MUST DASH."

I MUST DASH.

IT'S NOT MY ROUND, IS IT?
599.

600

I WISH YOU'D STOP GOING ON ABOUT HOW MEAN I'M SUPPOSED TO BE!

I BOUGHT THE LAST ROUND, YOU KNOW!

AND WHILE WE'RE ON THE SUBJECT, IT'S MY TURN WITH THE GLASS!

601

I'LL PROVE I'M NOT MEAN! WATCH THIS!

TWO BOTTLES OF BEST CHAMPAGNE, PLEASE!

I'M SORRY, SIR, WE'VE NONE LEFT...

...WHY NOT TRY A BOTTLE OF BEER, SIR? OH, WELL. IF THAT'S ALL YOU HAVE...

WHAT A MAGNIFICENT NIGHT, PIERRE!

DO YOU KNOW THAT THOSE STARS RULE OUR DESTINY? IT'S ALL THERE, YOU KNOW!

I BET YOU'RE A CAPRICORN!

SMACK!
602

I KNEW IT! WARM HEARTED KIND... YOU LIKE A GOOD JOKE...

YOU CAN DEFINITELY TELL SOMEONE'S PERSONALITY BY THE STARS, PIERRE.
603

TAKE MY DORIS, FOR EXAMPLE...

PLEASE TAKE HER! HAR! HAR! HAR-DE-HAR!

DEAR ME! SNIFF! OUR STAR SIGNS ARE CERTAINLY COMPATIBLE- THE WAY WE LAUGH AND JOKE TOGETHER!

SO YOU DON'T BELIEVE THAT I CAN READ THE FUTURE IN THE STARS?
604

OKAY! WHAT'S YOUR SIGN? IS IT CAPRICORN? ARE YOU A GOAT?

SMACK!

THERE YOU GO! I SAW THAT COMING!

Y'KNOW, SOMETIMES YOU CAN TELL A PERSON'S STAR-SIGN BY JUST LOOKING AT THEM!
605

TAKE ME, FOR INSTANCE. GO ON, HAVE A GUESS! WHAT D'YOU THINK I AM?

A BORING, FOUR-EYED LITTLE CREEP.

IT'S A GIFT!

COME ON! WHAT'S YOUR STAR-SIGN IN ASTROLOGY...
606

LISTEN, IF I HEAR ANOTHER WORD ABOUT ASTROLOGY, YOU'LL BE SEEING ALL THE STARS YOU WANT!

ALL THE STARS YOU WANT! A-HEH! HEH! HEH!
VERY GOOD.

THAT RULES OUT SCORPIO. THEY'RE FUNNY.

HOW DID THE NIGHT-SHIFT WITH MAD PIERRE GO?
FINE.

WE HAD A FASCINATING CHAT ABOUT ASTROLOGY. I THINK HE'S A VIRGO.
607

DON'T BE SMUTTY, DENNIS.

OKAY, EGON, JUST PICK OUT SOMEONE TO HELP YOU IN THE KITCHEN THIS WEEK.

A-HEH-HEH -HEH!
WHAT'S SO FUNNY?
608.

HA! HA! HAR!

HAR-HAR HAR-DE HAR!
HAVE YOU PUT A LAXATIVE IN MY DINNER AGAIN?

YOU MEAN I'VE GOT TO HELP YOU IN THE KITCHEN?
YUP.

BUT-BUT I CAN'T COOK!

609.

HERE AM I SAYING THAT TO A CHEF WHO FRIES JELLY.

YOU WANT ME TO PUT TWO EGGS IN THERE ?
YEAH.

TAP!
TAP!

HERE, THAT'S CLEVER!

I NEVER KNEW THE SHELLS CAME OFF!

ER... EGON?

THERE ARE ABOUT TEN COCKROACHES IN THIS SOUP.

OH, NO! IT'S RUINED!

THERE SHOULD ONLY BE SEVEN.

AND THIS, MY FRIEND, IS THE 'PIECE DE RESISTANCE'!

A LITTLE SOMETHING THAT SEPARATES A GREAT DISH FROM AN ORDINARY ONE.
CHOP! CHOP! CHOP!
6/12

WHAT, THE TOP OF A FINGER?

DO YOU KNOW THAT THE TOP CHEFS IN EUROPE WOULD KILL FOR SOME OF MY RECIPES?

SO, BEFORE YOU GO, I MUST INSIST ON TOTAL SECRECY.
6/13

REST EASY, EGON —YOU HAVE MY WORD.

YOUR '**WARTHOG SURPRISE**' IS SAFE WITH ME!

I SUPPOSE YOU'RE WONDERING WHY I GOT YOU IN HERE.

WELL, IT'S A TOP SECRET MISSION AND, IN MY OPINION, ONLY TWO MEN IN THIS FORT CAN PULL IT OFF!
6/4

HOWEVER, JUST FOR A LAUGH, I'LL LET YOU TWO HAVE A GO.

FIRST, YOU CROSS 'THE DEVIL'S KITCHEN'...

...UP OVER 'THE HEIGHTS OF HELL'... THROUGH 'SATAN'S SWAMP'... AROUND 'THE VALLEY OF DEATH'...
6/5

...AND FINALLY INTO 'DINGLY DELL'.

WELL, THIS IS IT, DENNIS.
CLUNK!

US AGAINST EVERYTHING THAT NATURE CAN THROW AT US.
616

WELL WE CAN TAKE IT — AND MORE! LET'S GO!

HANG ON. I'VE CAUGHT MY COAT IN THE DOOR.

HANG ON, DENNIS — WE'D BETTER CHECK THE MAP.

NOW, LET ME SEE, AH, YES...

...I KNOW WHERE WE WENT WRONG! A SLIGHT DIRECTIONAL MISTAKE...

...WE WENT TO THE PUB INSTEAD OF THE MAP-READING CLASS.
617

WHAT ARE YOU DOING?

WHEN WILL YOU EVER LEARN? GIVE ME THAT CANTEEN!

AND WHAT'S THAT YOU'RE EATING?
DRIED FISH.

EXACTLY! AND SINCE WHEN DO WE DRINK **RED** WINE WITH FISH?

RIGHT, DENNIS, PITCH THE TENT HERE.
TENT?

ER...THAT'S RIGHT. YOU'VE GOT IT WITH THE SLEEPING BAGS.
SLEEPING BAGS?

OH, THAT'S TERRIFIC! WHAT ARE WE GOING TO SLEEP IN?

I'VE GOT OUR PYJAMAS.

SINCE OUR ORDERS ARE TO SPY ON THE ENEMY, WE MUST GET AS CLOSE TO THEIR CAMP AS POSSIBLE.
620

DON'T WORRY! I'VE BROUGHT SOME CAMOUFLAGE JUST WATCH THIS!

COME ON THEN! WHERE AM I?

DENNIS, YOU'RE CAMOUFLAGED AS A BUSH.
YUP!
621

OFFHAND, DENNIS, HOW MANY BUSHES DO YOU SEE IN THE VICINITY?
NONE.

SHOWS YOU HOW GOOD THE CAMOUFLAGE IS!

AAH-CHOO!
622

DENNIS, WE'RE ALMOST AT THE ENEMY CAMP. FOR THE LAST TIME, GET RID OF THAT STUPID DISGUISE!

BE HONEST-WOULD YOU HAVE SPOTTED ME IF I HADN'T SNEEZED?

THERE'S THE ENEMY CAMP. I'LL MAKE SOME NOTES ON THEIR MOVEMENTS THEN WE'LL CLEAR OFF.

623

WHISPER.

I MEAN MOVEMENTS IN GENERAL, DENNIS. WE DON'T PLACE A GREAT DEAL OF MILITARY IMPORTANCE ON THEIR VISITS TO THE TOILET.

IT'S GOING TO BE TRICKY FINDING OUR WAY BACK TO THE FORT.
NO BOTHER!

ON THE WAY HERE I FILLED MY POCKET WITH SAND, RIGHT? WELL THERE'S A HOLE IN IT. WE JUST FOLLOW THE TRAIL HOME!

IF YOU LIVE TO BE A HUNDRED, DENNIS, YOU'LL NEVER BE CLOSER TO BEING STRANGLED.

DO ME A FAVOUR, DENNIS, AND GET RID OF THAT STUPID CAMOUFLAGE BEFORE WE GET BACK TO THE FORT.

SERGEANT!
HEY! YOU MADE IT!

WELL DONE! WE THOUGHT YOU WERE LOST!

WHAT ABOUT DENNIS? WAS HE CAPTURED?

I HAVE RETURNED, BROTHERS, AND I MUST READ YOU SOMETHING FROM THE ANCIENT MANUSCRIPTS!

"ANYONE BANISHED FROM THE TRIBE MUST:—
a) RETURN WITH THE HEAD OF AN ENEMY WARRIOR..."
626

...AND I MUST ADMIT I WAS A BIT SURPRISED WHEN I READ THE NEXT BIT—

"OR:—
b) RECITE A NURSERY RHYME OF THEIR CHOICE."

YOU MEAN I'M STILL BANISHED?
627

UNTIL YOU BRING US THE HEAD OF AN ENEMY WARRIOR.

ER... LISTEN, HOW WOULD YOU LIKE SOME MONEY?

STUFFED INSIDE THE HEAD OF AN ENEMY WARRIOR.

I'M A FAILURE.
628

OUTCAST BY MY PEOPLE, ALONE IN THE WORLD. DOOMED TO WANDER AIMLESSLY.

RUSTLE!

AND NOW SOMEONE'S EATEN ALL THE RED ONES.

I CAN'T GO ON LIKE THIS.

NOW IS THE TIME FOR ACTION! THE TIME TO TAKE LIFE BY THE THROAT!
629

MASTER OF MY OWN DESTINY!

I'VE COME OVER ALL DIZZY.

A HAWK SOARING IN THE SKY.
630

O, DENIZEN OF THE SKY! GIVE ME A SIGN!

GIVE ME A HANKY!

I WILL LET THE FATES DECIDE MY DESTINY. THE PATTERN OF THE FALLEN PEBBLES WILL BE MY GUIDE.

631

AHA! SO BE IT!

"GO DIRECTLY TO THE PUB."

A TRICK!
PICK A CARD, BEAU!

WHAT IS IT?
THE FOUR OF HEARTS

LET ME THINK... IT'S THE FOUR OF HEARTS!

AND BEFORE YOU ASK, I'M NOT TELLING YOU HOW IT'S DONE!

YOU'LL BE AMAZED AT THIS TRICK. TAKE THE ACE OF CLUBS.

NOW GIVE IT BACK TO ME.

AND HEY, PRESTO! THERE IT IS!

I'M STUNNED, DENNIS. YOU USE MIRRORS, PERHAPS? MAGNETS? MARKED CARDS?

NOT ANOTHER TRICK, DENNIS.
THIS ONE'S A BELTER!
634

NAME ANY TWO CARDS!
FIVE OF SPADES. TEN OF DIAMONDS.

NOW I MUST CONCENTRATE. YOUR TWO CARDS WERE THE FIVE OF SPADES AND THE...THE NINE OF... NO I CAN'T REMEMBER.

I'LL HAVE TO POLISH THAT ONE UP A BIT.

ONE DAY I'M GOING TO BE A PROFESSIONAL MAGICIAN.
OH, YES?
SHUFFLE

IMAGINE GETTING PAID FOR SAWING WOMEN'S LEGS OFF!

YOU'RE SUPPOSED TO SAW THEM IN HALF, DENNIS.
WHAT?

YOU'D NEVER GET THE SAW THROUGH THEIR HEADS.
635

I'VE GOT A NEW TRICK FOR YOU.
636

HOW MANY FINGERS AM I SHOWING?
TWO.

EXACTLY! HOW ABOUT THAT THEN?

I ALSO TRUST YOU NOTICED MY EYES WERE COVERED?

NOW THIS TRICK INVOLVES A HANKIE, A WATCH, A...
DENNIS!

I'VE HAD IT UP TO HERE WITH YOUR TRICKS! IF YOU MUST DO ONE, MAKE IT THE VANISHING TRICK!
637

RIGHT, THE VANISHING TRICK INVOLVES A HANKIE, A WATCH, A...

I'LL TELL YOU SOMETHING, DENNIS. WILL YOU PROMISE NOT TO GET EXCITED?
OKAY.

'VERA OF THE SEVEN VEILS" IS APPEARING IN TOWN TONIGHT.

MMMGLZRW!

I'LL RUN A COLD BATH FOR YOU, DENNIS.
MMMGLZRW!
638

ARE YOU READY YET, BEAU?

DENNIS, 'VERA OF THE SEVEN VEILS' WON'T BE ON FOR HOURS YET!

WELL, I'M GOING NOW. I WANT TO MAKE SURE I GET A GOOD VIEW.
639

I DON'T SEE HOW YOU CAN FAIL, DENNIS.

HERE WE ARE! I'M SO EXCITED!
TONIGHT
VERA OF THE SEVEN VEILS
GAO

DENNIS, BEFORE WE GO IN I'D LIKE TO GET A COUPLE OF THINGS STRAIGHT.

DURING OUR LAST VISIT TO SEE THIS LADY THERE WAS A CERTAIN LOSS OF DIGNITY.

AND THAT'S NOT ALL SHE LOST, MATE!

TONIGHT
VERA OF THE SEVEN VEILS
CAN'T WE MOVE A BIT NEARER THE STAGE?
NO, DENNIS.

I'M SURE WE COULD MOVE TOWARDS THE CENTRE A BIT.
WE'RE FINE HERE, DENNIS.

JUST AS LONG AS I CAN SEE ALL RIGHT.

HERE SHE COMES NOW SO FOR GOODNESS SAKE ACT IN A DIGNIFIED MANNER.
TONIGHT VERA OF THE SEVEN VEILS

YOO-HOO! VERA! IT'S ME, DENNIS! GOD, I LOVE YOU!
CLAP! CLAP!
YEEE-HAH! GIVE ME THAT OL' SOFT SHOE SHUFFLE!

SORRY, BEAU, WHAT WERE YOU SAYING?
CLAP! CLAP!

TONIGHT VERA OF THE SEVEN VEILS
I'M IN LOVE, BEAU!

BEAU, PLEASE REMEMBER THE NEXT FIVE MINUTES IN DETAIL.
WHAT? WHY?

CLUNK!

BECAUSE YOU'RE GOING TO FAINT.

WH-WHAT HAPPENED?
YOU FAINTED.
TONIGHT VERA OF THE SEVEN VEILS

DID SHE...I MEAN... HAS SHE...?
YEP! ALL SEVEN VEILS!

SHE WAS ONE HUNDRED PER CENT HEAD-TO-TOE STARKERS!

ANOTHER BRANDY, HASSAN.
TONIGHT VERA OF THE SEVEN VEILS

OH, THAT VERA! I WORSHIP HER!
FOR GOODNESS SAKE, DENNIS, WHAT DO YOU SEE IN HER? SHE IS A WOMAN OF THE NIGHT WITH DUBIOUS MORALS AND MINIMUM I.Q.

WHISPER
I WOULDN'T HAVE PUT IT QUITE LIKE THAT BUT, GRANTED, HER CHEST IS OF GENEROUS PROPORTIONS.

BEAU, WOULD YOU DO ME A FAVOUR?
WHAT?

WOULD YOU WRITE A LETTER TO VERA FOR ME?
OH, ALL RIGHT. WHAT DO YOU WANT TO SAY?
WHISPER

DON'T YOU WANT TO TALK ABOUT THE WEATHER OR SOMETHING BEFORE YOU ASK HER CHEST SIZE?

LET ME RECAP, DENNIS. THIS IS THE LETTER YOU WANT TO WRITE TO VERA.

"DEAR VERA, WHAT SIZE IS YOUR CHEST? LOVE, DENNIS."

OH, DEAR... IT DOESN'T SOUND VERY ROMANTIC, DOES IT?

I KNOW! PUT 'LOVE AND KISSES, DENNIS.'

BEAU, LOOK! IT'S A LETTER FOR ME - FROM VERA!

WHAT'S IT SAY? WHAT'S IT SAY?

"STOP BOTHERING ME, YOU LITTLE CREEP, OR I'LL HAVE YOUR FACE RE-ARRANGED."
648

ARE THERE ANY KISSES AT THE BOTTOM?

DENNIS, YOU'LL JUST HAVE TO ADMIT THAT YOUR ROMANCE WITH VERA WAS NOT TO BE.

IF ONLY SHE HADN'T ENCOURAGED ME.
649.

ER... TO BE FAIR, DENNIS, I DON'T THINK SHE ENCOURAGED YOU.

OH, YEAH? AND WHOSE GLASS OF WINE DID SHE PUT OUT HER CIGAR IN?

COR! IS THAT CHOCOLATE CAKE?
YUP.

D'YOU MIND IF I HAVE A BIT?
NOT AT ALL.

DELICIOUS! WHO MADE IT?

YOUR MUM, WASN'T IT PIERRE?

MY MUM MADE THAT CAKE.
AND VERY NICE IT WAS TOO.

THE POINT IS IT WAS MEANT FOR ME!

WHAT HAVE YOU GOT TO SAY?
CRACK!

THAT SHOULD SAVE ON THE WASHING-UP!

IS MAD PIERRE STILL ANGRY AT ME FOR EATING HIS MUM'S CAKE?
YES.
652.

HE SAID THAT WHEN HE GOES INTO A BLIND RAGE HE FORGETS EVERYTHING!

HE SAYS YOU'VE TO STAY AWAY FROM HIM TILL HE'S CALMER.

THAT WAY HE'LL BE ABLE TO REMEMBER THE NOISE OF YOUR BONES BREAKING.

KITCHEN
EGON!

YOU'VE GOT TO HELP ME! MAD PIERRE GOT A CAKE FROM HIS MUM AND I ATE IT AND NOW HE'S GOING TO KILL ME! MAKE ME ANOTHER ONE!
653

DON'T WORRY— I'LL MAKE ONE EXACTLY THE SAME AND HE'LL LET YOU OFF.

RIGHT! FIRST I'LL MAKE THE GRAVY FOR IT!

THAT'S THE BEST CAKE YOU CAN MAKE?

WELL I ONLY HOPE MAD PIERRE WILL ACCEPT THIS AS A REPLACEMENT FOR THE ONE I NICKED.

HE'LL LOVE IT! THERE'S A SURPRISE FOR HIM TOO!

I PUT A LUCKY COCKROACH IN IT!

DID YOU GIVE PIERRE THE REPLACEMENT CAKE?
YES.

WHAT DID HE DO WITH IT?

LET'S PUT IT THIS WAY— I'M GLAD THE CANDLES WEREN'T LIT.

HALLO! YOU MUST BE THE NEW BLOKE! I'M BEAU!
656

JINGS! AH'M HAMISH! HOW'S IT GOIN' YE WEE RASCAL?

AHA! I'D RECOGNISE THAT LILTING ACCENT ANYWHERE!

TELL ME, HOW IS CARDIFF THESE DAYS?

ER... HAMISH HERE HAS A JOKE TO TELL YOU, DENNIS.

...AN' THE OTHER COO SAYS "DINNIE SHOOGLE IT ABOOT!"

OH, NO! HAR-HAR! HAR-DE-HAR!
657

WHAT'S HE SAYING?

TELL ME HAMISH — I'VE ALWAYS WANTED TO KNOW WHAT A SCOTSMAN WEARS UNDER HIS KILT.

SOME DAE AN' SOME DINNIE, YE KEN, BUT IT'S NO' A SEMMIT! AN' IT DEPENDS, YE KEN.
658

THAT'S WHAT I THOUGHT, BUT I WASN'T SURE.

TELL ME HAMISH, WHICH PART OF SCOTLAND DO YOU COME FROM ?
AUCHTERMUCHTY.
659

OH, I SEE! THAT'S WHERE YOU COME FROM!

I THOUGHT HE WAS CLEARING HIS THROAT.

WHAT BRINGS YOU TO THE LEGION, HAMISH?

AH, WEEL IT WAS A LASSIE, YE KEN. SHE WAS AYE MOANIN' AN' GREETIN' "DAE THIS AN' DAE THAT"! AH WAS FAIR WAPPIT' WI' HER BLETHERIN'!

MAKE YOUR MIND UP, BEAU. YOU'VE EITHER GOT TO SAY "HARD LUCK" OR "WELL DONE".

I CAN'T UNDERSTAND A WORD HAMISH SAYS.
...THE NOO!

I'M GOING TO HAVE TO TELL HIM TO SPEAK SLOWLY AND IN THE QUEEN'S ENGLISH!

NOW LISTEN—
ARE YE FOR A WEE DRAM?

AYE, IT'S A BRAW, BRICHT, MOONLICHT NICHT THE NICHT, HAMISH!

MY MUM'S SENT ME A CHRISTMAS PRESENT. I WONDER WHAT IT IS?
SHAKE!
662

SHE'S JUST LIKE YOU, ISN'T SHE?
YUP!

IT'S PROBABLY A BOX OF SAND.

COME ON, THEN. WHAT'S YOUR MUM SENT YOU FOR CHRISTMAS?

IT'S AN EASTER EGG! HOW STUPID CAN YOU GET!
663

SHE KNOWS I DON'T LIKE THEM.

OO! I'VE GOT A SHOCKING HANGOVER!
SERVES YOU RIGHT FOR BEING SO SNEAKY.

DON'T THINK WE DIDN'T SPOT YOU NIPPING OUT OF THE ROOM AND COMING BACK IN THAT LITTLE BIT MERRIER.

I DARE SAY IF WE HADN'T STOPPED YOU, THE WHOLE PACKET OF WINE GUMS WOULD HAVE GONE.

ANOTHER YEAR DRAWS TO A CLOSE.

LET ME THINK— WHAT WAS MY GREATEST ACHIEVEMENT DURING THE LAST TWELVE MONTHS?

I KNOW! GETTING ALL FOUR STATIONS AT MONOPOLY!
CLICK!

I MUST MAKE A RESOLUTION FOR THE COMING YEAR.

"I WILL ENDEAVOUR TO WALK THE PATH OF LIFE IN AN HONEST, UPRIGHT AND UNDERSTANDING MANNER..."
666

"I'LL TRY AND GIVE UP SWEETIES."

I MUST APPROACH THE COMING YEAR, NOT WITH TREPIDATION, BUT WITH EXPECTATION!
667.

A GREAT STEP FORWARD INTO BETTER THINGS! INTO A NEW LIFE! INTO A WONDROUS FUTURE!
LEAP!

...INTO FRESH CAMEL DUNG.

IT IS TIME TO WELCOME THE DAWN OF A NEW YEAR.

I WILL CHANGE INTO THE ANCIENT CEREMONIAL COSTUME OF THE OCCASION.
668

BANG!
DAMN!

I HOPE IT'S ALL RIGHT WITH ONLY TWO BALLOONS.

RESOLUTION:—
I WILL TRY TO GIVE UP SWEETIES

WAIT A MINUTE—I DIDN'T SIGN IT!
669.

I DIDN'T SIGN IT!
CLICK

ALWAYS LEAVE A LOOPHOLE.
CHOMP! CHOMP!

MEN, I HAVE A VITAL JOB FOR TWO OF YOU...

...TWO FEARLESS BUT CUNNING HAND-TO-HAND FIGHTERS WHO WILL THRIVE ON A DIET OF DANGER AND EXCITEMENT!
670

PHEW! THAT'S A RELIEF—I WAS SURE IT WAS GOING TO BE US AGAIN!

US?!

BUT YOU SAID FOR THIS JOB, YOU WANTED FEARLESS HAND-TO-HAND FIGHTERS WHO THRIVE ON DANGER ETC.!
671

OH, I SEE! IT'S A JOKE! THE SERGEANT IS PULLING OUR LEGS! OH, HA-HA! WHAT A THIGH-SLAPPER, EH, DENNIS?

PLEASE TELL ME THE SERGEANT IS LAUGHING, DENNIS.

HERE, BEAU—THIS MISSION WE'RE GOING ON—WE'RE GOING TO GET LOTS OF MONEY FOR IT!
WE ARE?

I JUST HEARD THE SERGEANT SAY SOMETHING ABOUT US BEING VERY DEAR OR ON EXPENSES OR SOMETHING LIKE THAT!

OH, WHAT WAS THE WORD HE USED?
EXPENDABLE.
THAT'S IT! WE'RE EXPENDABLE!
CLICK!

WE'RE FAR ENOUGH FROM THE FORT—WE'D BETTER OPEN OUR ORDERS.

OH, NO! WE'VE TO INFILTRATE THE ENEMY CAMP AND WREAK HAVOC AS SABOTEURS!

WHAT DO MINE SAY?
I KEEP FORGETTING YOU CAN'T READ.

THEY SAY I'VE TO WAIT IN THE PUB TILL YOU'VE FINISHED.

OH, NO-WE'RE SURROUNDED!

RIGHT! YOU TAKE THE FIFTY ON THE RIGHT AND I'LL TAKE THE FIFTY ON THE LEFT! TAKE NO PRISONERS!

HAVE YOU BEEN DRINKING?

SURRENDER, YOU FOOLS! YOU ARE SURROUNDED!

NO, WAY, BUSTER! JUST TRY AND TAKE US!

SO BE IT! YOUR BLOOD WILL STAIN THE SAND!

YOU DO REALISE MY FRIEND HERE IS SPEAKING FOR HIMSELF?

WE WILL GIVE YOU ONE CHANCE TO LIVE.

ONE OF YOU MUST FIGHT OUR CHAMPION.

DENNIS, I'M MUCH BIGGER AND STRONGER THAN YOU ARE.

ON THE OTHER HAND, I WEAR GLASSES.
676

COME ON, THEN— WHERE'S YOUR CHAMPION? WE'RE READY!
677

ER...THERE YOU GO! SORT HIM OUT, DENNIS!

WHAT HAPPENED TO THE 'WE'?

YOU CAN BEAT THIS TINKERBELLE, DENNIS.

REMEMBER YOUR TRAINING. USE HIS BULK TO YOUR ADVANTAGE BY USING YOUR BODY AS A FULCRUM.

FAILING THAT, KNEE HIM IN THE GROIN.
678

YOU BEAT HIM, DENNIS! HOW DID YOU MANAGE IT?
679.

WELL, MY DAD WAS AN EXPERT AT KARATE.
AND HE TAUGHT YOU?

NO, HE SOLD ME HIS KNUCKLE-DUSTER.

YOU HAVE DEFEATED OUR CHAMPION.
680

YOU HAVE FOUGHT FOR YOUR LIBERTY AND FOUGHT WELL. IN ACCORDANCE WITH OUR ANCIENT TRIBAL LAWS, YOU ARE FREE TO GO.

MAY THE GODS FLY ON WINGS TO PROTECT YOU.

BEFORE I CHANGE MY MIND AND HAVE YOUR FACES RE-ARRANGED.

TWO SHOTS, THAT'S ALL I NEED.
681.

TWO CLEAN SHOTS TO END THIS HELL!

IT'S NO USE! I CAN'T DO IT!

LOOK, DENNIS! THE SERGEANT IS CRYING WITH RELIEF THAT WE'RE BACK!

GOOD DAY, MINE HOST! I'M LOOKING FOR SOMETHING SPECIAL TODAY!

I SEEM TO REMEMBER YOU SERVING UP A PARTICULARLY DELICATE LITTLE WINE – IT HAD A HINT OF SPARKLE AND A SUBTLE FLOWERY FRAGRANCE.

YOU MUST REMEMBER! THERE'S THE BURN-MARK WHERE I SPILLED SOME!

MAGNIFICENT! THIS IS THE STUFF!

DO YOU REALISE HOW LONG IT TAKES TO MAKE A CLASS WINE LIKE THAT? EH? D'YOU REALISE?

THE GRAPE-SELECTION, THEN FERMENTATION, TEMPERATURE-CONTROL, BOTTLING, MATURING...

...YOU'RE TALKING ABOUT THE BEST PART OF A WEEK!

HALLO, PIERRE! COME AND HAVE A DRINK!

IT'S A BIT SPECIAL AND THE MAKERS RECOMMEND YOU...ER...SIP A LITTLE AND LET IT...ER...ROLL ROUND THE PALATE...
684

CRASH!

...OR DRINK A FULL BOTTLE IN ONE GO! THAT'S ALL RIGHT TOO!

Y'KNOW, THERE'S SOMETHING ABOUT DRINKING WINE THAT GETS TO ME.

I JUST CAN'T HELP IT. BUT WINE MAKES ME WANT TO BREAK THINGS OVER PEOPLE'S HEADS!
685

WELL...ER...DON'T LET IT BOTHER YOU, PIERRE...I'LL...ER... GET THE DRINKS IN.

TWO SNOWBALLS, PLEASE.

PIERRE'S BEGINNING TO GET THAT WILD-EYED LOOK. I'D BETTER TRY TO DISTRACT HIM.

HOW'S THE WIFE, PIERRE?

SMACK!
686

STILL WITH THE MILKMAN, EH ?

BOY! THAT WAS SOME FIGHT YOU HAD IN THE BAR!

OH, THAT REMINDS ME! YOU KNOW THAT BLOKE WITH THE BIG, RED NOSE ?

HE WANTS IT BACK.
687

DEAR ME, YOU'RE AN UNCOUTH LITTLE DEVIL, AREN'T YOU?
CHOMP!

I BET YOU'VE NEVER EVEN GIVEN UP YOUR SEAT TO AN OLD LADY ON A BUS.
DON'T BE DAFT!

YOU MEAN YOU HAVE?

NO, I MEAN I'M NOT BETTING.

CHOMP! CHOMP!

WHAT TIME IS IT?

DENNIS, YOUR MANNERS ARE APPALLING!

OH, ALL RIGHT! WHAT TIME IS IT PLEASE?

DENNIS, DO YOU KNOW ANYTHING ABOUT ETIQUETTE?
NOPE.
690

WELL, ONE OF THE FIRST RULES IS 'DON'T TALK WITH YOUR MOUTH FULL'!

WHY'S THAT, THEN?

DENNIS, WOULD YOU LIKE ME TO TEACH YOU ABOUT ETIQUETTE AND MANNERS?
ALL RIGHT.

RIGHT, YOU'RE AT A PARTY, THE HOSTESS—AN ELDERLY, RICH COUNTESS—SAYS SOMETHING YOU DON'T QUITE CATCH, WHAT DO YOU SAY?

691

SPEAK UP, YOU OLD BAT!

I SEE. WE'RE HAVING OUR LITTLE JOKE, ARE WE?

I TELL YOU, DENNIS, WELL-MANNERED MEN ALWAYS ATTRACT WOMEN.
THEY DO?
692.

FOR EXAMPLE, HOW WOULD YOU ASK A YOUNG LADY OUT FOR THE EVENING?

WHISPER!

MIND YOU, I GET SLAPPED A LOT.

ALL THIS STUFF ABOUT ETIQUETTE AND MANNERS IS NONSENSE!

MY MUM TAUGHT ME ONE RULE AND I'VE NEVER FORGOTTEN IT!
693.

'DON'T POINT WITH YOUR MOUTH FULL'!

REMEMBER THAT AND THE WORLD'S YOUR OYSTER!

RECENTLY, THE ENEMY HAVE BEEN ANTICIPATING OUR EVERY MOVE.

THEY'RE GETTING INFORMATION FROM INSIDE THIS VERY FORT!

AND WE ALL KNOW WHAT THAT MEANS—
SPY!
HE SAID IT MEANS 'SPY'
OH, I SEE! I THOUGHT HE SAID 'MINCE PIE'
694.

...SO ALMOST CERTAINLY, THE SPY IS SOMEONE HERE!

ALL RIGHT, PEEP-OUT HERE! I HEARD THAT!
695

I SUPPOSE 'THE BUTLER DID IT' IS YOUR IDEA OF A JOKE.

I WONDER WHO THE SPY IN THE FORT IS?
696

CLUNK!

MAYBE IT'S EGON. MAYBE HE SMUGGLES OUT MESSAGES IN THE FOOD.

THERE'S A MESSAGE IN THIS LOT ALL RIGHT — DON'T EAT IT.

PEEP, I THINK WE'VE FOUND OUT WHO THE SPY IS. IT'S ONE OF THE SCOUTS.

YOU'VE GOT A WAY WITH WORDS — I WANT YOU TO TRY AND TRICK HIM INTO A CONFESSION.

DON'T WORRY, SARGE. I'LL GAIN HIS CONFIDENCE FIRST, THEN SLIP IN A TELLING QUESTION!

SO WHO'S A LITTLE PEEPING TOM, THEN?
697

ADMIT IT, ABDUL, YOU'RE THE SPY, AREN'T YOU?
YES, I DID IT.

DON'T DENY IT! WE CAN PROVE IT!
YES, I **AM** THE SPY.

OWN UP, ABDUL! THE GAME'S OVER! WHY NOT CONFESS!
I DID! I AM! I ADMIT IT!
6-98

HE'S A TOUGH COOKIE ALL RIGHT, BUT I THINK I CAN CRACK HIM, SARGE!
CLUNK!
CLUNK!

SPLAT!
6-99

SO EGON WASN'T THE SPY AFTER ALL?
NO.

YOU'RE SURE?
YES.

DENNIS, THERE ARE ***NO*** SECRET MESSAGES IN YOUR ALPHABET SOUP.

THIS IS THE BEST IDEA I'VE EVER HAD! PURE GENIUS!
700

THERE MIGHT BE ONE TINY SNAG BUT THEY'LL NEVER NOTICE IT!

THROW DOWN YOUR WEAPONS— I'M TAKING OVER THE FORT!
DON'T BE STUPID.

THEY'VE NOTICED IT.

YOU MUST BE JOKING!
701

NO— THIS IS A SIEGE!
BUT THERE'S ONLY ONE— YOU!

I HAD A FEW CALL-OFFS.

HERE ARE MY TERMS FOR ENDING THE SIEGE.
702

FIRST, GIVE UP YOUR ARMS, THEN A TOTAL SURRENDER OF THE FORT AND A COMPLETE WITHDRAWAL OF YOUR TROOPS FROM THE AREA.
NO!

HOW ABOUT A QUID AND I'LL GO AWAY?

HE'S CRAZY!

HE WANTS THE WHOLE FORT TO SURRENDER TO HIM...

...PLUS SAFE CONDUCT TO THE DESTINATION OF HIS CHOICE.

DON'T FORGET THE JELLY-BABIES.
AND A BAG OF JELLY-BABIES.
703

RIGHT! THAT'S IT! YOU'VE HAD FAIR WARNING! I'M GOING TO ATTACK!
704

HERE I COME! I'M GOING TO STORM THE WALLS!

MARK MY WORDS— IT'LL BE A BLOODBATH!

YOU'VE HAD IT! I'M COMING UP ANY MINUTE NOW!

YOU'VE FORGOTTEN YOUR LADDER, HAVEN'T YOU?

I'VE DECIDED TO STARVE YOU OUT. IT'LL BE A DIFFERENT MATTER WHEN YOU'RE ALL DRIVEN MAD WITH HUNGER!
705

CREAK!

CLICK!
CLICK!
CLICK
CLICK!
CLICK!

...SO THAT'S WHY I POPPED BY TO SEE IF YOU WANTED ANYTHING FROM THE SHOPS.

ANY SIGN OF PEEP?
ER... NO, SIR.

WELL HE BETTER NOT BE DRUNK AGAIN!
NOT BEAU, SIR! I'M SURE THERE'S A GOOD REASON HE'S LATE.
706

PSST! BERT? I'M AS DRUNK AS A FERRET! OPEN THE DOOR BEFORE FUNGUS-FACE SEES ME.

TSK! TEN DAYS FOR BEING DRUNK AND DISORDERLY.
707

THERE'S NO WAY I'M GONNA ROT AWAY IN HERE! I'LL MAKE A ROPE FROM THE SHEETS.

SKIPPING SHOULD HELP PASS THE TIME.

HAH! LITTLE DO THEY KNOW I MANAGED TO HIDE MY PEN-KNIFE!

I'LL MAKE A GUN FROM THIS BLOCK OF WOOD AND FOOL THE GUARD.

HERE HE COMES! BOY, IS HE IN FOR A SHOCK!
RATTLE!
708

THAT'S GOOD! A SHIP, IS IT?

VISITOR FOR YOU, PEEP.
RATTLE!
709

HERE, BEAU, I'VE BROUGHT YOU A CAKE.
GOOD OLD DENNIS! THERE WILL BE A FILE INSIDE!

I'D BETTER WATCH MY TEETH WHEN I BITE INTO THIS, EH?
NUDGE NUDGE!
WINK WINK!

YOU'RE NOT KIDDING— EGON MADE IT.

THAT'S IT! THE PERFECT PLOT!
CLICK!
710

I'LL HIDE UNDER THE BED THEN WHEN THE GUARD COMES IN HE'LL THINK I'VE ESCAPED AND I CAN WALK OUT!

OH, NO! SERGEANT! QUICKLY!

WHAT IS IT?
BEAU'S STUCK UNDER HIS BED.

RIGHT, PEEP– YOU'RE FREE TO GO.
WELL, BEFORE I DO, I'VE A FEW THINGS TO SAY!

THE WALLS IN HERE ARE STREAMING WITH DAMP AND —
711

PEEP, DO YOU WANT ANOTHER TEN DAYS INSIDE?

—AND I WONDERED WHO TO THANK FOR LAYING ON THE RUNNING WATER.

Y'KNOW, DENNIS, IT'S FUNNY HOW LIFE TURNS OUT.
7/12

I REMEMBER AS A YOUNG LAD IN MUSIC CLASS DREAMING OF BECOMING A GREAT CONDUCTOR.

SIGH!

I SUPPOSE THE ONE-MAN BUSES PUT AN END TO ALL THAT.

WHAT DO YOU THINK YOU'D BE DOING NOW, DENNIS, IF YOU WEREN'T IN THE LEGION?
7/13

OH, I DON'T KNOW. I WAS ALWAYS PRETTY GOOD WITH MY HANDS.

PROBABLY A PICK-POCKET.

Y'KNOW, DENNIS, I SOMETIMES FEEL THAT LIFE HAS PASSED ME BY.
7/4.

BUT FOR ONE CRUEL TWIST OF FATE, I COULD HAVE BEEN A CONCERT PIANIST!
WHAT WAS THAT?

I COULDN'T PLAY THE PIANO.

YOU CAN'T ALWAYS TELL WHAT PEOPLE DO BY THE WAY THEY LOOK.
7/15.

TAKE MAD PIERRE- HE PROBABLY USED TO STUFF TEDDY-BEARS!

HA! HA!— AARGH!

DOWN PEOPLE'S THROATS.

WHERE DID YOU WORK BEFORE YOU JOINED UP, PIERRE?
A SLAUGHTERHOUSE.
7/16

THAT'S... ER...NICE. WHAT HAPPENED?
I GOT SACKED AFTER TWO HOURS.

I WAS ENJOYING MYSELF. I'D SLAUGHTERED ABOUT A HUNDRED...

...TURNS OUT THERE WAS A MACHINE I SHOULD'VE BEEN USING.

LIKE I SAY DENNIS, YOU CAN NEVER TELL A PERSON'S JOB BY THE WAY HE LOOKS.
7/17

GLOOP!

I MEAN, WITH A HAT LIKE THAT YOU'D THINK EGON WAS A COOK.

COME!
COLONEL ESCARGOT
7/8.

AH, PEEP! HOW ARE YOU AT SECRETARIAL WORK?
NOT REALLY MY LINE, SIR...

AH, WELL. I SUPPOSE YOU'D BETTER GO ON THE MARCH WITH THE OTHERS.

... BUT I TRY TO SCRAPE BY ON 200 WORDS A MINUTE!

RIGHT, PEEP. TAKE THIS DOWN.

"DEAR...." OH, WHAT'S THE NAME AGAIN?

DON'T PROMPT ME! IT'S ON THE TIP OF MY TONGUE!
7/9.

AND DO YOU, GEORGE ESCARGOT, TAKE THIS WOMAN, NANCY— **THAT'S IT! *NANCY!***

THIS IS A TOP SECRET ADDRESS, PEEP. I WANT YOU TO READ IT AND MEMORISE IT.

720

DONE IT ?
YES, SIR.

THANK GOODNESS! IF THE WIFE KNEW ABOUT HER SHE'D KILL ME.

NOW'S MY CHANCE WHILE THE COLONEL'S OUT !

I'VE ALWAYS WANTED TO READ MY FILE AND SEE IF THEY THINK I'M OFFICER MATERIAL !
721

I DIDN'T KNOW 'SNIVELLING' HAD TWO 'L'S

I WONDER IF I SHOULD ALTER MY FILE?

WHY NOT? I'LL JUST MAKE SLIGHT ALTERATIONS TO THE UNFAVOURABLE COMMENTS.

HOW DO YOU SLIGHTLY ALTER "UTTERLY BRAINLESS IDIOT"?

HI, BEAU, HOW DID YOUR WEEK AS THE COLONEL'S SECRETARY GO?
NOT BAD.

DID YOU KNOW THAT THEY HAVE FILES ON EVERYONE? EVERY SHRED OF INFORMATION THAT COULD DETERMINE THE FUTURE PROMOTION PROSPECTS AND HOPES OF US ALL!

WOW! WHAT HAVE THEY GOT ABOUT ME?

YOUR COLLAR SIZE.

LETTER FOR YOU, BEAU.

MORE SPIDERY SCRAWL FROM THE PAW OF DORIS.

A DIFFERENT SCENT, THOUGH— LESS EXPENSIVE.
SNIFF!

STOUT INSTEAD OF GIN.
724.

I WONDER IF I SHOULD READ DORIS' LETTER NOW?
725

NO, I'LL WAIT TILL TONIGHT WHEN I CAN SIT DOWN ON MY OWN AND GET SOME PEACE.

NO POINT IN THROWING UP IN PUBLIC.

I SUPPOSE I MIGHT AS WELL READ THIS LETTER FROM DORIS.
7-26

Dear Beau,
When I think of us together again, my heart pounds like mad!

MINE TOO!

...and I had the enclosed photo taken just for you.
All my love,
Doris x

WHAT AM I DOING? THIS IS BEDTIME!

IT WOULD BE LIKE EATING A POUND OF CHEESE!
7-27

I WONDER IF I SHOULD LOOK AT THE PHOTOGRAPH DORIS SENT ME.

I MEAN, IT'S AMAZING WHAT CAN BE DONE WITH A TASTEFUL BACKGROUND AND SUBTLE LIGHTING.
728

STILL, IT'S BETTER NOT TO TAKE CHANCES.

WHAT ARE YOU DOING?
I'VE JUST BURIED DORIS' PHOTOGRAPH. GOD, IT WAS REVOLTING.

WHY DIDN'T YOU JUST TEAR IT UP... OR BURN IT?

I DID THAT AS WELL.
729

I WISH I WAS CLEVER LIKE BEAU.

HE CAN TALK FOR AGES ABOUT ALL SORTS OF CLEVER THINGS.

EVEN RIGHT NOW, I BET HE'S THINKING ABOUT SOMETHING REALLY AMAZING.
I WONDER WHERE I LEFT MY JELLY BABIES?
730

BEAU, DO YOU THINK YOU COULD TEACH ME TO BE CLEVER?

I WANT TO BE ABLE TO DISCUSS POLITICS AND THINGS. MAYBE BECOME A LAWYER OR A DOCTOR!
731

OKAY, I'LL TEACH YOU BUT DON'T SET YOUR TARGETS TOO HIGH. WE'VE GOT TO EASE YOU INTO IT!

NOW, WHEN I THROW THIS STICK...

NOW, IF YOU WANT TO BECOME CLEVER, DENNIS, YOU'LL HAVE TO TALK ABOUT THINGS LIKE MUSIC.
732

FOR EXAMPLE, WHO'S YOUR FAVOURITE COMPOSER?

PHEW, THAT'S A HARD ONE. I DON'T KNOW REALLY...

WHO WROTE **'HICKORY DICKORY DOCK'**?

YOU SEE, DENNIS, IT'S OFTEN ABOUT **APPEARING** CLEVER RATHER THAN **BEING** CLEVER.

I GET IT! USING BIG WORDS AND THAT!
EXACTLY!

LIKE **"KEYHOLE"**
'KEYHOLE'?
733

MAYBE NOT. I DON'T WANT TO LOSE THEM COMPLETELY.

COME ON, BEAU— TEACH ME A BIG WORD I CAN USE TO MAKE PEOPLE THINK I'M CLEVER.

WELL, GIVE ME A CLUE! WHAT WOULD YOU LIKE THE WORD TO BE ABOUT?

WHISPER
7-34

WORDS OF THAT NATURE ONLY HAVE FOUR LETTERS, DENNIS.

THERE'S THE COLONEL. GO AND TRY OUT THAT BIG WORD I TAUGHT YOU ON HIM!

EVENING, SIR! IT'S AN IMMACULATE NIGHT!
7-35

IT CERTAINLY IS! WITH ALL THE UNPARALLELED SPLENDOUR OF TROPICAL PULCHITRUDE!

YOUR NOSE IS RUNNING.

HAIL! WISE CHIEFTAIN OF MY TRIBE!

TO END MY BANISHMENT, YOU HAVE TOLD ME TO BRING THE HEAD OF AN ENEMY WARRIOR. I WONDERED IF, PERHAPS, YOU COULD SET ME AN EASIER TASK?
736

ALL RIGHT. BRING US THE HEADLESS **BODY** OF AN ENEMY WARRIOR! *HA! HA!*

I WONDER IF I COULD SMACK HIM IN THE MOUTH BEFORE HIS MEN GOT ME?

THEY SAY BEING ALONE IN THE DESERT CAN PLAY FUNNY TRICKS ON THE MIND.
737

THANK GOODNESS NOTHING LIKE THAT HAS HAPPENED TO ME!

NO, MY BRAIN'S JUST AS SHARP AS EVER.

JUST AS WELL WITH ALL THESE DAMN HEDGEHOGS ABOUT.
SWIPE!

I NEED FRESH WATER.
738

LUCKILY, I'M A NOMAD AND I KNOW THE ANCIENT WAYS OF FINDING WATER.

IT'S ALL TO DO WITH AIRWAVES AND FEET POSITIONING.
SHUFFLE!

ANYONE GOT A DRINK?

GREETINGS, MY FRIENDS! MAY I SHARE YOUR WATER?
OH, WE'RE "FRIENDS" NOW ARE WE? I TAKE IT YOU'RE THIRSTY.
739

WHAT ABOUT ALL THE TIMES YOU TRIED TO ATTACK US, MURDER US, THEN CHOP OUR HEADS OFF?

OH, I SEE. YOU'RE GOING TO BE PETTY ABOUT IT.

WHAT WILL YOU GIVE US IN EXCHANGE FOR SOME WATER?
MY TRIBE HAS THE SECRET OF ETERNAL LIFE. I WILL LET YOU HAVE IT.
COO! GIVE HIM THE WATER, BEAU!
740

WELL, COME ON! WHAT IS IT?
GLUG! GLUG!

KEEP BREATHING.

HAH! THOSE LEGIONNAIRES ARE FOOLS!

I TELL THEM THE SECRET OF ETERNAL LIFE AND THEY SCOFF!
741.

WHAT WAS IT THAT THE ANCIENT MANUSCRIPTS SAID ABOUT SUCH UNBELIEVERS?

IT WAS SOMETHING ABOUT TWO SHORT PLANKS...

BEFORE WE GO IN, LET'S TRY TO GUESS WHAT'S FOR DINNER.
CANTEEN
OH, I DON'T KNOW.
742

COME ON! GUESS!
I DON'T KNOW! BOILED GIRAFFE!
DON'T BE A SPOILSPORT! HAVE A PROPER GUESS!

YOU KNOW FINE WE DON'T HAVE THAT TWO DAYS RUNNING!

EGON! COME HERE!
743

THAT IS REVOLTING! IT'S BURNT, IT'S DRY AND TASTELESS! WHAT ON EARTH IS IT SUPPOSED TO BE?
FUMBLE!

IT'S NOT SUPPOSED TO BE ANYTHING— THAT'S THE ASHTRAY.

YOU CERTAINLY KNOW SOME FANCY DISHES, BEAU.

GIVE ME THAT AGAIN AND I'LL MAKE A NOTE OF IT.
744

...AND CUT INTO EQUAL STRIPS OF LENGTH...

THEN DIP THEM INTO YOUR EGG. THEY'RE CALLED "SOLDIERS."

WHAT AN ENJOYABLE BOWL OF SOUP!

BUT YOU HAVEN'T TOUCHED IT.

WELL, IT DIDN'T SEEM RIGHT...

NOT WHILE THE FLYS' INDIVIDUAL MEDLEY WAS GOING ON.
745

DOH! I FEEL AWFUL.
SNIFFLE!

AND IT'LL BE LUNCHTIME SOON AND THAT BEAU WILL BE MOANING ABOUT MY COOKING AGAIN! SNIFF!
746

I'VE A GOOD MIND NOT TO LET HIM HAVE ANY OF THIS SOUP.

C'MON, PEEP! JUST COMPLAIN ONCE MORE!

EGON!
OH, THANK YOU!

HA-HAR! ANY COMPLAINTS ABOUT THIS CAKE, PEEP?
747

I WOULD SAY THE ICING'S A BIT RUNNY.

RIGHT, MEN, WE DIG IN HERE!

WE MUST HOLD THIS POSITION AT ALL COSTS!

THE ENEMY MUST NOT PASS!

HERE WE WILL DO OR DIE IN GLORY! WE WILL PROTECT THIS SOIL WITH OUR BLOOD!

FOR HONOUR, FOR DEATH, FOR THE LEGION!

YES, WHAT IS IT, PEEP?

I WONDER IF YOU WOULD CHECK MY FOXHOLE FOR SPIDERS.
53
2